THE PLAY

Based on the gr8read novel *Alligator*
by Theresa Breslin

Adapted by

Theresa Breslin and Julie Gormley

Thresea Breslin is a winner of the Carnegie Medal. She is the author of over 30 books. Her work has been filmed for TV and made into radio plays. She has written for a wide age-range, from pre-school to young adults. Her books have been translated into more than 20 languages and are read world-wide.

Julie Gormley has retired from teaching after 30 years as a Principal Teacher of English and 4 years as a Staff Tutor. At the moment she is taking up a second career as a writer and literary consultant.

Y822. 914

First published in 2009 in Great Britain by
Barrington Stoke Ltd
18 Walker St, Edinburgh, EH3 7LP

www.barringtonstoke.co.uk

ISBN: 978-1-84299-643-0

Printed in Great Britain by Bell & Bain Ltd

Introduction

I was chatting to a group of teenagers about story-writing. I told them of a news item I'd read in the papers about someone trying to sell an alligator at a car boot sale. We talked about what kind of person might do that and what kind of person would end up taking the alligator home.

The book has become a best seller. It has been just as much fun turning it into a play as it was to write the original.

Theresa Breslin

I enjoyed adapting Alligator into a play. It was a challenge. It was really important to make sure that the dialogue was right for the individual characters in the book. Suspense had to increase as the play went on, until the final twist at the end. I chose to have a narrator to describe the action a bit more and to expand on the dialogue. The narrator also has some funny comments to make.

Julie Gormley

This play is for Callum and Campbell Jude
T.B.

This book is for Tony and Kathryn
J.G.

Theresa Breslin and Julie Gormley would like to thank the following for their help with this play:

From St Ninian's High School, Kirkintilloch, teacher Caroline Harper and her students:

Ciaran
Connor
Gerry
Grant
Kevin
Mark
Megan
Melissa
Natalie
Patrick
Roxy
Shannon
Shaun

From St Thomas Aquinas School, Glasgow, teacher Mick Gormley and his student Shannon

Contents

Cast

Narrator

Male or female. Jono's friend, but more street-wise. She/he has a good sense of humour.

Crusher

Older than Jono. He is cunning and used to getting his own way.

Jono

The hero. A nice, trusting lad.

Jono's mum

A widow, with a new boy friend, **Sam**. She
cares about Jono and wants the best for her
son.

Sam

Jono's mum's new boy friend, a kind man who
wants to gain Jono's trust and respect.

Thief

A small-time burglar.

Policeman

An older officer who thinks he's seen it all
and knows everything.

Policewoman

A young trainee officer: smart, with a sense of humour.

Extras

ALSO: if wanted, extras could be used at the car boot sale, or a crowd could gather outside the lock-up garage. It would be quite easy to give some of them small speaking parts by adding to the text at these points. Let the actors make up their own comments.

Scene 1

At the Car Boot Sale

The stage could be bare apart from a table mid-stage. On it is a large brown box. ALSO: there could be several tables with people gathered round them buying and selling.

(The narrator enters. He or she walks to the side of the stage and speaks to the audience.)

Narrator: Did you ever get yourself mixed up in something you didn't want to do? We've all done that. Well, I know I have. But nothing

quite as crazy as my mate
Jono. That's Jono over there.

*(Jono enters and stands at the other side of
the stage from the narrator.)*

Narrator: Sometimes he gets himself
into a bit of a mess, does
Jono. Take last week at the
local car boot sale ...

*(Crusher enters and stands beside the table
in the middle of the stage.)*

Crusher: Pssst! Wanna buy an
alligator?

Jono: What?

Narrator:	That's Crusher standing there with the big box. He's the kind of guy you don't want to mess around with ... if you value your life.
	Yes, Crusher.
	Whatever you want, Crusher.
	Three bags full, Crusher.
	No one ever says no to Crusher. No one, and I mean no one, even *thinks* of saying no to Crusher.

(The narrator leaves the stage.)

| Crusher: | Over here! Quick! I've got something here, just for you, Jono. |

Jono: What? What is it?

Crusher: Look, Jono. Look inside!

(Crusher lifts the lid. Jono's eyes grow big. His mouth falls open with shock. He takes a step away, but Crusher grabs his arm and pulls him back to the table.)

Jono: An all ... alli ... gator! No way, Crusher.

Crusher: Hold on, Jono. An alligator is a great pet, so it is. Who wants a dog or a cat or a rabbit when they can have an alligator? An alligator's ... well ... very rare. You'll be the first to have one. And if you don't like it you can always make it into a pair of shoes ... or a suitcase ... or maybe a handbag!

Jono:	If it's so great, why are you selling it?
Crusher:	What do you mean?
Jono:	Why are you selling this alligator if it's such a great pet?
Crusher:	I'm selling it for a friend.
Jono:	Where did he get it?

Crusher:	His mum brought it back from Australia or China or somewhere.
Jono:	What? I don't believe you.
Crusher:	I know, I know. Most mums bring back a T-shirt or a baseball cap. But my pal's mum got him this alligator. Now he don't want it, and he asked me to sell it for him.
Jono:	How did his mum get it past the security checks at the airport?

Crusher: She put it in a shopping bag,
             so she did.

Jono: That can't be right. You can
             hardly get *people* past
             airport security checks now!

Crusher: She came off a boat. It's
             different with boats. And
             she fed it some of her
             sleeping pills so that it
             didn't move. They must
             have thought it was a soft
             toy or something.

*(Crusher lifts the box from the table and
places it on the floor, slides the lid to one
side and pulls Jono over to look at it again.)*

Crusher:	You can pat it if you like. Go on. Don't be scared. It won't harm you.

(Jono reaches into the box with care and pats the sleeping alligator.)

Jono:	What's it called?

Crusher:	It's an alligator, so it's called an ALL - I - GA - TOR!

Jono:	I know it's an alligator. I mean, has it got a name?

Crusher:	You buy it, Jono. You can call it what you like ... Jaws!

Gnasher! You could always call it after me ... Crusher.

Jono: I'm not buying an alligator. What would I do with an alligator?

Crusher: It would be a very different sort of pet. No one else would have anything like it.

Jono: And *I'm* not going to have anything like it either. Just think what my mum would say if I came home with an alligator!

Crusher: I'll only charge you a fiver.

Jono: A fiver! You must be joking.

                   You'd have to give *me* a fiver

                   to take that alligator off

                   your hands!

(Crusher pulls a fiver out of his pocket and
thrusts it into Jono's hands.)

Crusher: Done!

(Crusher kicks the box over to Jono and then
runs off stage. The narrator walks back onto
the stage.)

Narrator: Well, that's how it all began.

                   But there's more to come.

                   Lots more!

(The narrator walks to the front of the stage. Jono is looking puzzled.)

Narrator: So Jono went home with his large brown box. What was he to do with the alligator? How could he keep the secret from his mum? AND – how long would it take for the sleeping pills to wear off?

Scene 2

At Jono's House

There is a sofa in the centre of the stage. To the left there is a dining table with a computer, and two chairs. To the right there is a TV with a coffee table beside it.

(Jono is sitting at the computer looking at the monitor. The light shines on the narrator as he or she comes in and takes up his or her place at the side of the stage.)

Narrator:	When Jono got home, his first move was to put the alligator in the garden shed. Clever move, eh? That gave

him time to think up a plan.
You'd like to know what sort
of plan, wouldn't you? So
would Jono.

*(The light rises on Jono and fades on the
narrator. Jono is seated at the table, talking
to himself. He is working on the computer
and reading some of the words out loud.)*

Jono: How do you spell it again?

A-L-L-Y. G-A-T-E. T-O-R.

Is that right? Can't be ...

What does the screen say?

"Do you mean

A-L-L-I-G-A-T-O-R?"

I guess I do. Great! Got a website now! Facts about alligators – let me see ...

(*Jono runs his finger over the screen as he tries to make sense of the words. He starts to read the first entry but soon stops.*)

Jono: In the wild, alligators will attack ... *No!*

(*He reads the second entry on the screen.*)

Jono: Alligators can eat – *Oh, no!*

(*He hears the front door open and close and knows his mother is home. He shakes his head and mutters.*)

Jono:	Oh, no. No. No.

Mum:	Hi, Jono. Had a good day? Anything interesting happen?

Jono:	No, Mum, just a normal day.

(Mum pulls off her shoes and wiggles her toes.)

Mum:	My feet are killing me. I'm too tired to cook tonight. Fancy something from the chippie?

Jono:	Fine, Mum. I'll go.

Mum:	What's that you're doing?
Jono:	Er, em … it's a school project.

(Mum comes over to Jono to see what he is doing.)

Mum:	Oh, right … Alligators? It's good that the project is about something you'd want to know about. You always liked animals, even when you were a little boy.
Jono:	So why did you never let me have a pet?

(Mum looks sad, as she always does when she talks about Jono's dad.)

Mum: Your dad had allergies, and then, and then ... he died. I'm out at work every day and you're at school. I suppose you're older now, and if you promised you'd take proper care of a pet ...

Jono: I would ... I would ...

(Mum looks more cheerful. She even laughs.)

Mum: I'll think about it. As long as you don't ask me for a pet alligator!

(Jono's eyes pop out.)

Mum: I'm not joking now, Jono.

How about a small pet?

Maybe a guinea pig or a

hamster? Something *small*

… Something *tame* …

Something *safe*.

(Jono's mum exits, carrying her coat and her shoes. The stage goes dark and the narrator is lit up by a spotlight. He or she is still standing at the side.)

Narrator: Doesn't look good for Jono,

does it? Off he went to the

chippie, trying to think up a

plan. He couldn't tell his

mum about the alligator in the garden shed. No, it was his mess and he would have to find his own way out of it. Listen! Do you hear anything?

(Crashing noises are heard from offstage and there is the sound of snapping teeth.)

Narrator: Uh-oh! Something has woken up!

(The narrator looks offstage. He or she falls back in mock terror. A scream is heard off-stage. The narrator puts his or her hands over his or her eyes in horror.)

Narrator:	Oops, Jono. Time for some quick thinking!

(The noises suddenly stop.)

Narrator:	That's Jono's take-away gone. The fish supper. The pizza. The chips with curry sauce. *And* the boxes they came in. Well, the alligator seems happy for the moment. It's falling asleep again – but it won't be for long! Now Jono needs to go back to the chippie and use the cash Crusher gave him to buy another take-away.

(The lights fade from the narrator and come up on the dining table where Jono and his mother are sitting. Mum begins to clear away the plates.)

Mum: Sam's coming round later, Jono. I hope you don't mind. He works so hard. He's never away from that lock-up garage.

Jono: Oh! Sam's lock-up garage ...

(Jono sits up. It looks as if he's just had a good idea. The doorbell rings and Mum goes to answer it.)

Mum: That sounds like Sam now.
I'll let him in.

(Sam enters and puts his keys on the dining table beside the computer, while he keeps a DVD in his hand.)

Sam: Hi, Jono! I've got a great new DVD here. I thought we could watch it together. It's a horror movie called *Alligator Attack*. It's about a family who live in Florida. There's a great scene where the alligators attack ...

(As Jono begins to reply, he moves over to the table and quietly picks up Sam's keys with his homework folder. He nods to his mum.)

Jono: I've got to go out for a while. To see a mate. From school. To check a bit of that project. Just go ahead and watch it with Mum, Sam.

Sam: I thought we could watch it together.

Jono: I've got stuff to do. I'll come back later and see the end of it with you.

(Sam is a bit upset.)

Sam: Please yourself, Jono.

Jono: I won't be long.

Mum: I've never known Jono to

               work so hard at his

               school-work, Sam. Was that

               the shed door banging?

Sam: Don't worry, love. He'll be

               back before you know it.

*(Sam and Mum put the DVD on and relax on
the sofa. Slowly their heads fall back and
they nod off as the film goes on.)*

*(Jono creeps in softly while Mum and Sam are
sleeping and drops the keys onto the coffee*

table. He sits down on the floor in front of

the TV.)

Narrator:	Well, you can guess what Jono's done, can't you? Yes, Jono put the half-asleep alligator into his rucksack and carried it round to Sam's lock-up garage. When he got there, he dropped the alligator into the car pit. He knew that would give him some more time to think about what he might do with the alligator ... At least, that's what he thought. But

things didn't turn out like
that.

(The stage goes dark and then Sam, Mum and Jono are lit up by a spotlight. Sam's mobile goes off and Sam leaps to his feet, still half asleep.)

Sam: Lock the door! The alligators are on the loose! Phone for help!

(Sam wakes up properly, a bit red in the face.)

Sam: Hm, sorry, what is it?

Mum: It's your mobile, Sam.

(Sam listens to the message on his mobile.
He looks shocked.)

Sam: It's the police. There's a spot
                    of bother at my lock-up! I'll
                    need to go round there right
                    now.

Mum: I wonder what's happened.
                    You go ahead, Sam, and we'll
                    follow.

(Jono grabs the keys from the coffee table
and hands them to Sam. The stage goes
dark.)

Scene 3

At the Lock-Up Garage

(The stage is bare. An older policeman and a young policewoman enter with the thief between them. The thief struggles to free himself. ALSO: there could be people looking on, making comments, if extras are needed.)

Policeman: You're nicked, pal.

Thief: I haven't stolen anything. Search me if you want. I've got nothing. Let me go.

Policewoman: No one said anything about theft, sir. The charge will be

that you broke into and
entered that lock-up garage.
You're coming with us.

Thief: Charged! You're kidding.
                The owner of the lock-up
                ought to be charged. There's
                a dangerous animal in there.
                It almost killed me.

Policeman: You can't fool us, pal. Seen
                it all and heard it all before.
                You're coming with us ...
                now!

Thief:	Stop! No, listen! There's a monster in there! A giant alligator!
Policeman:	And I'm Santa Claus and this policewoman here is the fairy godmother. Do you think my head zips up the back, pal?
Policewoman:	Sir, maybe we'd better have a quick look.
Policeman:	Look, dear, I've heard every story in the book. Every thief has a tall tale to tell ... but this one beats them all.

Policewoman: Still, it'll only take a few
                    seconds to look …

(Sam enters, running, holding his keys.)

Sam: I'm Sam Smith, the owner.
                    Is anything missing? Did he
                    get the car? Is it damaged?

Thief: The car damaged? The *car*
                    damaged? What about me?
                    Your alligator could have
                    killed me – eaten me alive!

Sam: An alligator? What
                    alligator? That's rubbish! I
                    don't have an alligator in
                    there. No one in their right

mind would keep an alligator in a lock-up. And believe me, I'm in *my* right mind.

Thief: I'm telling you the truth. Take a look for yourselves if you don't believe me.

Policeman: If there's an alligator in there, I'm Indiana Jones and I'll eat my hat!

(Jono and his mum run in to join Sam and the Policeman.)

Mum: What's happened? Is everything all right, Sam?

Jono: No one's been hurt, have
                 they?

Sam: Everything's fine. The police
                 found a thief trying to steal
                 something from my lock-up
                 and now he's making up
                 some story about being
                 attacked by an alligator.

*(The policeman jokes and laughs and takes
out his notebook.)*

Policeman: You don't mind coming with
                 me, sir? I'll just get ready to
                 take down this alligator's
                 details. I need to get its age,

place of birth, size, colour of eyes ... and all that.

(He walks off-stage with Sam. There is a scream. Sam and the Policeman come running back.)

(The policeman is rubbing his eyes and scratching his head.)

Policeman: It *is* an alligator. If I hadn't seen it with my own eyes ...

Sam: How did it get in there?

Policewoman: It doesn't matter how it got in there. It's how we get it out that matters. I'll contact

the zoo and ask their advice.

(The policewoman turns to Sam.)

Policewoman: I'm sure an alligator is a lot

better than a guard dog, sir.

But I'm not sure it's legal to

keep it in your garage.

(The policewoman walks over to the
policeman, takes off his hat and hands it to
him.)

Policewoman: I hope you're hungry, sir. I

know that you're not Indiana

Jones, but you did say you

would eat your hat. Do you

want salt and vinegar with it?

(The narrator enters.)

Narrator: So the police took the thief away. And the zoo people arrived and took the alligator away. Aww! A neat ending, isn't it? I like neat endings, except ... that's not the end of the story. Jono got off the hook. Yes. The thief was charged. Yes. Nothing was stolen from Sam's garage. Well, would *you* take on an alligator?

Scene 4

Back at Jono's House

The stage set is as before for Scene 2.

(Jono is seated at the table with his computer. Sam and Mum are seated on the sofa. Mum is looking puzzled.)

Mum: You know, there's something bothering me.

(Jono and Sam look at each other.)

Mum: I find it a bit odd, Jono, that you were checking facts about alligators on the Internet tonight. Then an

40

alligator turns up in Sam's
lock-up garage. Is there
anything you want to tell
me?

Sam: Oh, leave Jono alone! Where
            would he get an alligator
            from?

*(Mum looks as if she still suspects something
but shrugs her shoulders.)*

Mum: I'll make some tea, but
            you're not off the hook yet,
            Jono. I think there's
            something fishy going on.

(Jono tries to look as if it's got nothing to do with him, and turns the computer on as Sam comes up softly behind him.)

Sam: I know it was you, Jono. You can't fool me so easily. When I came in this evening I left my keys on the dining table right next to the computer, but when we were going to the lock-up, you picked them up from the coffee table. I'm not going to say anything to your mum. But you've got to tell me – what's the story?

(The Narrator enters.)

Narrator: Jono told Sam what had
happened, right from the
start. There was something
about Sam that he trusted.
And ... it wasn't as if he had
a choice, did he?

(The Narrator exits.)

Sam: Well, that's some story – you
hiding that alligator in my
lock-up. You know, if it
hadn't been for you, my car
would have been stolen.
That would have cost me a

lot of money. So, thanks a
lot, Jono.

(He slips a £20 note into Jono's hand.)

Jono: Hey, thanks, Sam, you're a
real pal.

Sam: But that's not all. You know
how you always wanted a
pet? Well, I'm going to get a
dog to guard the lock-up and
you can take care of it for
me. Don't worry, I'll OK it
with your mum.

Jono: Wow, a dog!

(The narrator enters as Jono exits.)

Narrator: There's another small
surprise. When Jono cleared
up the mess the alligator left
in the shed, he found
something in the box.
Something special.
Something very special.
Something very, very
special. Something he could
use to pay Crusher
back. Something to make
sure that he'd never be
taken in like that again.

(Jono enters carrying a box, nicely wrapped up with a big bow on the top.)

(Enter Crusher stage left.)

Crusher: Hi, Jono. I want a word with you. I heard you got a reward from the zoo for finding that alligator.

Jono: Sure did, Crusher. You know, I don't know how to thank you ... for the fiver you gave me, and the alligator. And my reward. And my dog. And –

Crusher: Cut out the thanks, Jono.

You know, I've been thinking
... I should have a share in
your good luck. So ...

(Crusher grabs the box out of Jono's hands.)

Crusher: I'll just take this. What is
it – perfume, jewellery,
chocolates? It'll make a nice
present for my girlfriend, or
for me.

Jono: So it will, Crusher. So it will.

*(Crusher starts to undo the bow on the box.
Jono pauses for a moment and then speaks to
the audience.)*

Jono: It's a present he'll never

forget.

(Crusher pulls out a large white egg. He
stares at it for a moment in stunned silence,
and then in alarm as it begins to crack open.)

Jono: I found that in the box the

alligator came in. It's an egg

– an egg that's just about to

hatch out!

A large white alligator egg!

(Crusher struggles to hold the egg as it begins to crack open and bits of shell fall to the floor. Then Crusher jumps back as if his hand has been bitten and starts to scream his head off.)

Crusher: Aaaaahhhhhhhhhhh!!!!!!!!!!!!

The End

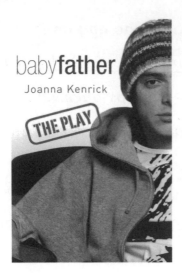

Babyfather: The Play
by
Joanna Kenrick

I'm pregnant!
Micky's girlfriend is pregnant.
Mickey is 15.
Is there a way out? Or is Mickey going to be a dad?

Perfect: The Play
by
Joanna Kenrick

Too good to be true?
Dan and Kate are perfect together.
Nothing can go wrong.
Until the lying starts ...

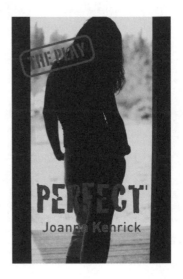

Blade: The Play
by
Chris Powling

Stay away from Toxon.
That's what they tell
Rich. They tell him
about Blade too, and
what it can do to you.
But Rich is in the wrong
place at the wrong time

Thing: The Play
by
Chris Powling

Black button eyes.
Ziz-zag mouth.
Stiff body.
Thing.

Once it was Robbie's
best friend. Now it's
become his enemy ...

You can order these books directly from our website at
www.barringtonstoke.co.uk

Alligator

(Original novel)

Jono's got a problem. He's just got himself an alligator. His mum is going to kill him. Unless the alligator gets there first ...

Mutant

Someone is trying to destroy the data and steal the work in the Clone Unit. But who is it and why are they doing it? Anything could happen if the research gets into the wrong hands. So who can Brad trust?

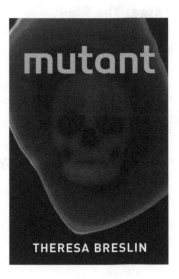

You can order these books directly from our website at
www.barringtonstoke.co.uk